Real-World Reading Comprehension

Grades 3–4

Strengthen the Reading Skills
Needed in Everyday Life

by Greta Neese Forrer

and

S. Michael Putman

Carson-Dellosa Publishing Company, Inc.

Greensboro, North Carolina

About the Authors . . .

Greta Neese Forrer has taught fourth grade for over six years. She has a bachelor's degree in elementary education from Ball State University. Greta is a member of the Golden Key National Honor Society and Kappa Delta Pi.

S. Michael Putman is a fourth-grade teacher. Michael earned a master's degree in early childhood and elementary education from Ball State University. He is a member of Pi Lambda Theta and Phi Kappa Delta. Michael is currently a doctoral candidate in elementary education with a reading concentration.

Credits

Editor
Sabena Maiden

Layout Design
Jon Nawrocik

Artists
Jon Nawrocik
Bill Neville

Cover Design
Christian Olsen

Cover and Inside Photos
Photo www.comstock.com
© 1993 Digital Wisdom, Inc.
© 2001 Brand X Pictures
© 1999 EyeWire, Inc. All rights reserved

Printed in the USA • All rights reserved.

ISBN 0-88724-946-9

Table of Contents

About This Book...

Real-World Reading Comprehension was written to help teachers strengthen the reading skills that students need every day. The activities in this book add realistic meaning to students' lives by providing common situations in which they read, analyze, and evaluate items, such as a birthday party invitation, camp application, or restaurant menu.

This book contains fourteen varied real-world reading selections. After reading each passage, students complete a series of questions to demonstrate comprehension. With every reading selection, there are two reproducible pages of comprehension questions, each containing fifteen questions. The first page is presented in an open-ended format, in which students write their answers in complete sentences. The format of the second page is mixed; multiple-choice, true/false, short-answer, and fill-in-the-blank questions are included.

The two different question formats allow the teacher several options. She can give all students open-ended questions or assign all students mixed-format questions. If the teacher chooses, she can use both formats. For example, she could assign the even-numbered questions from the open-ended format and odd-numbered questions from the mixed format. Or, she could give some students the first format and other students the second format. This provides ways to make modifications for students who may need them. An entire class can work on the same activity, with the same numbers, at the same time, while modifications are made for the students who need it. Also, to accommodate students' various writing-space needs, the teacher can have students write answers directly on the reproduced page, on a separate sheet of paper, or on the back of the reproduced page.

Each selection is followed by theme-based extension activities, writing prompts, and literature selections. This enables teachers to further integrate each theme into the curriculum and vary the activities according to students' needs. There is no specific order in which this book must be used. It can be used as a complete nonfiction environmental-print unit or can easily be incorporated into the existing language arts curriculum.

As students use the activities in this book, they will begin to feel more confident when they encounter everyday reading opportunities. Students will also begin to recognize the relevance of their reading skills beyond the classroom.

The Ridgeville Review

Indiana Life

◀ **SHE DID WHAT?** | **4D**
Reaction to Alice Sampson's decision to return the wallet.

www.ridgevillereview.com

Sunday, December 22, 2002

Section **D**

Honesty Pays

Girl returns wallet and finds a big reward.

Atlanta —

BY ANNE LONGLUNGER
Accommodating Press

RIDGEVILLE, Ind. - Alice Sampson, age 10, has learned that honesty does pay. Two weeks ago Alice was shopping with her mother when she noticed a wallet sticking out from under a clothing rack. When Sampson opened the wallet, she found more than $2,000 inside.

"I couldn't believe it! I had never seen that much money before!" said Sampson. Sampson reported that she thought about keeping the wallet, but just for a second. "I knew that I would return it because keeping it wouldn't be right. What if someone really needed that money for medicine or a doctor or something?"

After talking with her mother, Sampson returned the wallet to the store office. Less than two hours later, Mr. Albert Humphries came back to the store frantically looking for the wallet he had lost.

Humphries was surprised that his wallet had been turned

HUMPHRIES

Alice Sampson's decision to turn in the wallet has brought her newfound fame and fortune. Upon Sampson's return to school, she was greeted with a hero's welcome.

in untouched. "It was unbelievable! I am so grateful that someone honest found my wallet," he said.

Humphries wanted to thank Alice Sampson. He gave her a $100 cash reward for turning in the wallet. However, Humphries wanted to do something more for the girl. He set up a fund to pay for Sampson's future education. "If Alice decides to go to college, she won't have to worry about

where the money is going to come from," said Humphries.

Alice Sampson and her family are very thankful that Albert Humphries is such a generous man. "He didn't have to give me anything. I turned in his wallet because it was the right thing to do. I wouldn't have been able to sleep at night if I had taken his wallet," said Sampson.

See **HONESTY** | **4D**

Name ___Joseph___

Honesty Pays

Using the newspaper article, answer the questions in complete sentences.

1. Who wrote this newspaper article?

2. What is the name of this newspaper?

3. What is the title of this article?

4. Who is this article mainly about?

5. In what city did these events take place?

6. On what date was this article printed?

7. The events of this article took place when?

8. About how much money did Alice find?

9. Where did Alice find the wallet?

10. What did Alice do with the wallet?

11. What two things did Albert Humphries do for Alice?

12. Alice called Albert Humphries a generous man. What does *generous* mean?

13. Why did Alice turn in the wallet?

14. Do you agree with Alice's actions? Why or why not?

15. What would you do if you found a wallet?

    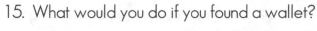

Name _Joseph_ 9570

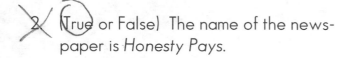

Honesty Pays

Use the information from the newspaper article to answer the questions.

1. Who wrote this newspaper article?
   a. Alice Sampson
   b. Accommodating Press
   (c.) Anne Longlunger
   d. Albert Humphries

2. (True or False) The name of the newspaper is *Honesty Pays*.

3. (True or False) The title of the article is "Honesty Pays."

4. Who is this article mainly about?
   (a.) Alice Sampson   b. Anne Longlunger
   c. Albert Humphries d. Anne Sampson

5. The events in the article took place in the city of _Ridgville_ .

6. On what date was this article printed?
   (a.) December 22   b. two weeks ago
   c. December 21   d. December 20

7. (True or False) The events in the article actually took place one month ago.

8. About how much money did Alice find?
   a. $2,000,000   b. $2
   (c.) $2,000   d. $200

9. Where did Alice find the wallet?
   In the store, under the rack

10. What did Alice do with the wallet?
    a. kept it
    (b.) turned it in at the store office
    c. gave it to her mother
    d. gave it to Albert Humphries

11. (True or False) Albert Humphries gave Alice $100 and set up her college fund.

12. Alice called Mr. Humphries a generous man. What does *generous* mean?
    (a.) giving   b. happy
    c. angry   d. friendly

13. Why did Alice return the wallet?
    a. She doesn't like to shop.
    b. Her family made her return it.
    (c.) She felt it was the right thing to do.
    d. The manager asked her to return it.

14. Do you agree with Alice Sampson's actions? Why or why not?

15. What would you do if you found a wallet?

Honesty Pays

Extension Activities

1. Many news articles include pictures that make the story more interesting to the audience. Draw a picture to go with the article about Alice Sampson. Include a caption to explain to the readers exactly what is happening.
2. Write a new title for the article you read about Alice Sampson. Remember that the title must support the main idea of the story, and it should also grab the reader's attention.
3. In the news article, Alice says that Albert Humphries is a generous man. How can you become more generous? Make a list of ideas. After you complete your list, select your best idea and try it out on someone.

Writing Prompts

1. Write a news article using a real-life story that you have experienced titled "Honesty Pays." Remember that the title should support the main idea of the article.
2. In the news article, Alice considers Albert Humphries to be a generous man. Do you know anyone who is generous? What is a generous person like? In what ways does a person show generosity?
3. Become a reporter for a day! Think of something going on in your school or classroom that you would like to write a news article about. Remember that reporters need to answer these questions: who, what, when, where, why, and how. After you have answered these questions, write a news article that will help keep your classmates informed about what is going on in your school.

Literature Selections

Kennedy Assassinated! The World Mourns: A Reporter's Story
by Wilborn Hampton (Candlewick Press, 1997).

Twelve-Year-Old Vows Revenge! After Being Dumped by Extraterrestrial on First Date
by Stephen Roos (Delacorte Press, 1990).

Write On Rosy! A Young Author in Crisis
by Sheila Greenwald (Minstrel Books, 1988).

Washington Elementary
December Lunch Menu

Monday	Tuesday	Wednesday	Thursday	Friday
2 turkey & noodles, mashed potatoes, green beans choice of banana or orange	**3** beef burritos, Spanish rice, corn choice of pudding or apple	**4** cheese pizza, potato chips, salad choice of ice cream or peach	**5** grilled cheese, tomato soup, crackers choice of mixed fruit or fruit-juice boxes	**6** cheeseburger, potato wedges, corn choice of pudding or peanut butter cookie
9 pancakes with syrup, sausage pattie choice of assorted fruits or fruit-juice boxes	**10** No Lunch Served 1/2 day for students	**11** hamburger, french fries, carrots choice of pear or chocolate chip cookie	**12** fish sticks, macaroni & cheese, green beans choice of orange or apple	**13** spaghetti, breadstick, salad choice of applesauce or pudding
16 ham, scalloped potatoes, peas choice of sugar cookie or pudding	**17** hot dog, coleslaw, baked beans choice of ice cream or apple	**18** pepperoni pizza, potato chips, salad choice of mixed fruit or banana	6-11 servings	

School will close for Winter Break after classes December 18. Classes will start again January 6.

Each day there is an entrée choice of a PBJ sandwich or a salad in addition to (but not included with) the hot lunch.

How many servings of the grains food group should you eat each day? (Look under the snowflakes for the answer.)

Don't forget to eat 2–3 servings from the dairy and meat/protein groups each day.

Students may choose juice or milk. Dessert is served with each lunch.

Washington Elementary

Using the school lunch menu, answer the questions in complete sentences.
(Note: The menu first lists the entrée, then side items #1 and #2, then dessert choices.)

1. The lunch menu is for which month?

2. On which day is there no lunch served?

3. When do classes resume after Winter Break?

4. Where can you find the answer to the question about the grains food group?

5. How many daily servings should you eat from the meat/protein and dairy groups?

6. What is special about December 10?

7. Write the two side items for December 12.

8. Why aren't there any lunch choices for December 7, 8, 14, or 15?

9. When does school close for Winter Break?

10. Which vegetable is served as a side item most often?

11. What kind of burrito is being served on December 3?

12. On how many days is fruit or something made with fruit offered?

13. Pepperoni is part of which food group? (It is one of the groups listed on the menu.)

14. Salad is served as a side item on which dates?

15. Which meal on the lunch menu would you be most likely to choose? Why?

Washington Elementary

Use the information from the school lunch menu to answer the questions.
(Note: The menu first lists the entrée, then side items #1 and #2, then dessert choices.)

1. The lunch menu is for which month?
   a. January   b. March
   c. December   d. not listed

2. Lunch will not be served on
   _____ .

3. (True or False) Classes resume after Winter Break on February 6.

4. Where can you find the number of grain servings needed per day?
   a. top of the menu   b. near the snowflakes
   c. near the tape   d. on the back

5. How many servings should you eat from the meat/protein and dairy groups?
   a. 2-3   b. 1
   c. 3-5   d. none

6. Why is lunch not served December 10?

7. The side items offered December 12 are
   _____
   and_____ .

8. Why does the menu not show any lunch choices for December 7, 8, 14, or 15?

9. School closes for Winter Break after classes on which day?
   a. December 18   b. December 2
   c. December 10   d. December 4

10. (True or False) Potatoes are the most common vegetable in the side items.

11. What kind of burrito is being served on December 3?
    a. cheese   b. chicken
    c. beef   d. bean and cheese

12. On how many days is fruit or something made with fruit offered?
    a. 1   b. 10
    c. 5   d. 7

13. (True or False) Pepperoni is in the meat/protein group.

14. List the dates salad is served with hot lunch.

15. Which meal on the lunch menu would you be most likely to choose? Why?

Extension Activities

1. Research information about the six food groups on the food pyramid. Build your own coat-hanger food pyramid, which shows foods from each group, by hanging the appropriate food pictures from strings.
2. Design a week-long school lunch menu. Be sure to include servings from each level of the food pyramid on four of the five days. Include how much you would charge for meals, snacks, and extras (such as additional food choices and second helpings).
3. Talk to your teacher about taking a class tour of the cafeteria to experience what the cafeteria workers must do to prepare for each day. The cafeteria manager could talk to your class to explain all of her duties.

Writing Prompts

1. Should students be able to ask for certain meals to be served in school? Why or why not? What would you want served? Why?
2. Write a persuasive letter to the cafeteria workers to try to convince them to add one of your favorite meals to the menu.
3. Why should people eat foods from all the different groups? Do you eat a balanced diet? What can you do to improve your eating habits?

Literature Selections

Captain Underpants and the Invasion of the Incredibly Naughty Cafeteria Ladies from Outer Space by Dav Pilkey (Scholastic, 1999).

101 School Cafeteria Jokes by Jovial Bob Stine (Scholastic, 1990).

102 School Cafeteria Jokes by Michael J. Pellowski (Watermill Press, 1992).

Something Queer in the Cafeteria by Elizabeth Levy (Hyperion Books for Children, 1994).

Wonder Kid Meets the Evil Lunch Snatcher by Lois Duncan (Little, Brown & Company, 1988).

A Game of Context Clues

Exploring the Universe™

Materials
Game Board, 1 Die, Answer Key, Storage Box, 60 Challenge Cards, 8 Game Pieces, 60 Asteroid Cards, Game Rule Sheet

Number of Players
You can play with 2–8 players. Also, one person will need to be chosen as the Answer Key Keeper. (The person with the Answer Key must not be a regular player.)

Object of the Game
The object of the game is to be the first person to start at the Space Station, travel around the universe, and land on Earth.

Challenge Cards
The player must read the sentences on the card and choose the definition that best states what the underlined word means.

Rules
1. Each player selects a game piece and places it at the Space Station.

2. The youngest person playing goes first. Play continues to the left of that player.

3. The player rolls the die and moves the number of spaces showing on the die.

4. As you play, you will find Asteroid Boxes. When you land on an Asteroid Box, pick a card from the Challenge Card pile. Read the sentences carefully. Choose the definition on the bottom that gives the best meaning for the underlined word.

5. The Answer Key Keeper will check to see if you are correct.

6. If your answer is correct, pick an Asteroid Card. It will give you directions. YOU decide if you want to follow the directions. For example, if the directions state that you lose a turn, you might choose NOT to follow them. If the directions state to move ahead a space, you probably would decide to do it.

7. If your answer is wrong, the Answer Key Keeper can pick an Asteroid Card. The Answer Key Keeper reads the card, then chooses one player who MUST follow the directions on the Asteroid Card.

8. When you are finished with the Asteroid Card and the Challenge Card, place them on the bottom of the appropriate card pile.

9. The game continues until a player lands on Earth. The Earth space (finish) must be reached by an exact roll of the die. The first player to reach Earth is the winner.

Optional Rule
Challenge Cards may be read aloud or silently.

Exploring the Universe

Using the game rules, answer the questions in complete sentences.

1. What is the name of this game?

2. How many people can play at one time?

3. Which materials are supposed to be included with this game?

4. What special condition has to be met for a player to arrive back on Earth?

5. How do you decide which player goes first?

6. When do you pick a Challenge Card?

7. Where do players place their game pieces at the beginning of the game?

8. If an incorrect answer is given, what happens?

9. If you gave a correct answer and the Asteroid Card instructs you to move back, what would you do?

10. What is the optional rule?

11. What does *optional* mean?

12. How does the game end?

13. How does a person win the game?

14. Why do you think game directions are important to read?

15. Which material could be missing without affecting the play of the game?

Exploring the Universe

Use the information from the game rules to answer the questions.

1. (True or False) The name of this game is Space Station.

2. How many people can play at one time?
   a. 2–12   b. 8
   c. 28   d. 2–8

3. Which materials are supposed to be included with this game?

4. (True or False) A player must reach Earth with an exact roll of the die.

5. (True or False) The player who rolls the highest number goes first.

6. If a player lands on _____, he picks a Challenge Card.
   a. an Asteroid Box   b. a planet
   c. the sun   d. a red space

7. Players place their game pieces on _____ to begin.
   a. Earth   b. the Space Station
   c. Start   d. any planet

8. If you answer incorrectly, the Answer Key Keeper picks an _____ .

9. (True or False) If you give a correct answer and the Asteroid Card tells you to move back, you MUST move back.

10. (True or False) Players must always read the Challenge Cards aloud.

11. There is one optional rule. *Optional* means _____
_____ .

12. How does the game end?
    a. A player reaches Earth.
    b. A player answers five Challenge Cards.
    c. A player gets to the Space Station.
    d. A player reaches any planet.

13. The first person to land on _____ wins.
    a. Earth   b. Mars
    c. an asteroid   d. the start space

14. Why do you think game directions are important to read?

15. Which material could be missing without affecting the play of the game?
    a. answer key   b. die
    c. storage box   d. game board

Exploring the Universe

Extension Activities

1. Create a new type of game. Begin by planning your ideas on paper. It could be a board game, a video game, or another type of game. How will someone win the game? What will the name of the game be? What materials will the players need to play the game? After you finish planning, write directions for your game and build it.

2. Make an advertisement for the game that you created in activity #1 or an existing game that you like to play. Begin by thinking about what you like about that game. Be sure to include those details in your advertisement. Provide a description of the game that will make others want to play it.

3. Do research to find out what types of games are popular in different parts of the world. Choose one game and demonstrate for your class how it is played. Include information about the country where the game is played.

Writing Prompts

1. Technology has changed our lives in many ways. How has technology changed the types of games that people play?

2. Different people enjoy different types of games. Write about a time you really enjoyed a game and a time that you really disliked a game. What made you feel these ways?

Literature Selections

Board and Card Games by Ruth Oakley (M. Cavendish, 1989).

Jumanji by Chris Van Allsburg (Houghton Mifflin, 1981).

New World by Gillian Cross (Holiday House, 1995).

Playing Marbles by Julie Brinckloe (Morrow Junior Books, 1988).

Power and Glory by Emily Rodda (Greenwillow Books, 1996).

Sidewalk Games Around the World by Arlene Erlbach (Millbrook Press, 1997).

Saturday Only

8 A.M.–10 A.M.

Sale **$9.99**
All Kids'
Athletic Tees
Sizes S–L
Reg. $34

fashion

Save **66%** on Kids' Jackets and Coats
(excludes collections)

Sale **$49.99** Boys' or Girls' Leather Jackets
Reg. $90–$145 (Sizes 8–20)

Save an extra **50%** on all backpacks
(Total Savings of 65%–75%)
Sale $9.99–$24.99

electronics

Save **50%** on all 13" color TVs
Reg. $250, Sale $124.99

Save an extra **10%** on CD Players
Reg. $19.99–$349.99, Sale $17.99–$314.99

Save an extra **50%** on Rugged Racer,
Cool BMX, or Zapitron video games
(Total Savings of 75%)

toys

Sale **$129.99**
Gentry Train Sets
Reg. $199.99, Save $70

Lowest Price of the Season!

Sale **$29.99** All Scooters
Were $39.99–$49.99, Orig. $74.99–$89.99

66% Off

All Tops and
Skirts for Girls
Sale $7.48–$13.60

All Bikes
$49.99
Reg. $145–$230

Extra 50% Off

All Bike Helmets
Sale $10.99–$25.50,
Total Savings of 60%

SCHOOLMAN'S
more for less.

Get-Up-Early Specials

Using the sale circular, answer the questions in complete sentences.

1. What day of the week is this sale?

2. Why is this sale called "Get-Up-Early Specials"?

3. List four items that are exactly 66% off.

4. What is at the season's lowest price?

5. What is the regular price of athletic tees?

6. What are the three main categories of sale items?

7. According to the sale circular, how many times have scooter prices been reduced?

8. Which video games are on sale?

9. What is the total percentage saved on bike helmets?

10. How long does this sale last?

11. Which item is regularly $250, and what is the sale price?

12. If you brought $200 to this sale, what item(s) would you buy? Why?

13. How many items have listed regular prices which are more than $200?

14. Based on the prices listed, on which item could you save the largest dollar amount?

15. Which two items share the same listed sale price and could have the same regular price?

Get-Up-Early Specials

Use the information from the sale circular to answer the questions.

1. What day of the week is this sale?
   a. every day   b. Friday
   c. Saturday   d. weekdays

2. Why is this sale called "Get-Up-Early Specials"?

3. List four items that are exactly 66% off.

4. What is at the season's lowest price?
   a. Gentry train sets b. backpacks
   c. leather jackets   d. scooters

5. (True or False) The regular price of athletic tees is $34.

6. Fashion, electronics, and _____ are the main categories of items on sale.

7. According to the sale circular, the price of scooters has been reduced _____ times.
   a. 1   b. 6
   c. 3   d. 2

8. List the video games on sale.

9. The total savings on bike helmets is ____ .
   a. 60%   b. 40%
   c. 66%   d. 50%

10. (True or False) This sale lasts for three hours.

11. (True or False) The 13" TV is regularly $250.

12. If you had $200, what would you buy at this sale? Why?

13. How many items have listed regular prices which are more than $200?
    a. 8   b. 1
    c. 3   d. none

14. Based on the prices listed, the largest dollar amount can be saved on _____ .
    a. scooters   b. tops and skirts
    c. CD players   d. 13" TVs

15. _____ and _____ share the same sale price and could have the same regular price.

Get-Up-Early Specials

Extension Activities

1. Practice using various computation skills with word problems created from the prices and sale percentages listed in the sale circular. For example, if Marissa's mom wants to buy her daughter three skirts and a bike helmet at Schoolman's sale, how much will she spend?
2. Have a sale in your classroom. You and your classmates can make money and "shop" for items. By doing this, you will make decisions based on how much money you have and how much you want to spend. Student cashiers can practice making change based on their classmates' purchases. Your teacher could be the store owner who oversees all of the "money" transactions.

Writing Prompts

1. Why is having a sale important to someone who is buying items and to the store owner who is selling items?
2. Why do sales occur more around holidays than at any other time during the year?
3. Describe items that you would like to see listed on sale in a circular and tell why it is important to you that each item be placed on sale.

Literature Selections

Annabelle Swift, Kindergartner by Amy Schwartz (Orchard Books, 1988).

In One Day by Tom Parker (Houghton Mifflin, 1984).

The Kids' Complete Guide to Money by Kathy S. Kyte (Alfred A. Knopf, 1984).

Money by Benjamin Elkin (Children's Press, 1983).

Number Mysteries by Cyril Hayes and Dympna Hayes (Penworthy Publishing, 1987).

The Phantom Tollbooth by Norton Juster (Random House, 1961).

Eagle Elementary Supply List

The items on this list are needed for school but are not included in regular school fees. All supplies should be at school by August 29. Please put your child's name on all supplies unless otherwise noted.

First Grade and Second Grade
inexpensive pair of tennis shoes for PE
tissues (large box)
school box for art supplies — about 7" x 11"
(24) #2 pencils — sharpened
2 spiral notebooks (2nd grade only)
crayons (at least 16 colors)
3 bottles glue — 4 oz. bottles (no names)
5 glue sticks — .77 oz. (no names)
children's dull craft scissors*
markers — set of 8 (thick) classic colors
4 solid-colored folders (2 pocket)
book bag
clipboard
1 package colored pencils (12 count)
3 packages lined 3" x 5" cards
watercolor paints
Boys — 1 box of gallon-size storage bags
Girls — 1 box of sandwich-size storage bags

*Second-grade scissors can have points.

Third Grade
inexpensive pair of tennis shoes for PE
crayons (minimum 24 colors)
glue or glue stick
#2 pencils (minimum 5)
1 package colored pencils
erasers
tissues (large box)
ruler (inches and centimeters)
3 packs <u>wide-ruled</u> notebook paper
school box for art supplies, 8" x 5" x 2"
6 solid-colored folders (2 pocket)
scissors
2 red pens
markers — set of 8
2 spiral <u>wide-ruled</u> notebooks (50 pages)
book bag

Fourth Grade and Fifth Grade

inexpensive pair of tennis shoes for PE
1 dozen #2 pencils
1 package colored pencils (12 count)
2 red pens
crayons (24 count)
markers — set of 8
2 packs <u>wide-ruled</u> notebook paper
2 <u>wide-ruled</u> spiral notebooks (70 pages)
ruler (inches and centimeters)
scissors — 5" with pointed tip
washable school glue — 4 oz. bottle
2 glue sticks

2 rolls transparent tape
2 packages 3" x 5" index cards — lined
tissues (large box)
school box for art supplies, 8" x 5" x 3"
10 folders — assorted plain colors (2 pocket)
calculator
book bag
clipboard
compass and protractor (5th grade only)
Last names A-M — glue pens
Last names N-Z — 4-pack of paintbrushes

• Please check regu

Eag

Eagle Elementary

Using the school supply list, answer the questions in complete sentences.

1. How many grades are in this school?

2. Will students receive all of the supplies needed when they pay school fees?

3. Should second graders put their names on their glue sticks? Should fifth graders?

4. What size glue bottle should a first-grade student purchase?

5. Why do you think each child's name should be on most of his supplies?

6. What is important about the notebook paper for third through fifth grades?

7. How do you know that the answer to #6 is important?

8. List two items that every student must have.

9. What is the difference on the supply list for first-grade boys and girls?

10. Why are the fourth-grade and fifth-grade supplies combined into one list?

11. Billy is in fourth grade. His sister is a fifth grader. When they buy school supplies, what differences will there be?

12. How can second-grade scissors be different from first-grade scissors?

13. First-grade students need twenty-four #2 pencils. What two things must be done before bringing them to school?

14. An 8" x 5" x 2" school box is needed for third grade. Why must it be a certain size?

15. Why do students need inexpensive tennis shoes at school for PE?

Eagle Elementary

Use the information from the school supply list to answer the questions.

1. (True or False) There are only four grades at Eagle Elementary.

2. (True or False) Students receive all supplies when school fees are paid.

3. Should second graders put their names on their glue sticks? _____
   Should fifth graders? _____

4. What size glue bottles should a first grader purchase?
   a. .77 oz.   b. 3 oz.
   c. 4 oz.   d. 5 oz.

5. Why do you think each child's name should be on most of his supplies?

6. What is important about the notebook paper for third through fifth grades?
   a. It is wide ruled.   b. It has 70 pages.
   c. It is white.   d. nothing

7. You know the answer to #6 is important because it is _____ .

8. (True or False) Students in every grade must have a clipboard and a book bag.

9. First-grade boys and girls have one difference on their list. What is it?

10. Why are the fourth-grade and the fifth-grade supplies combined into one list?

11. (True or False) Billy is a fourth grader; his sister is in fifth grade. His sister needs a compass and protractor; Billy will not.

12. (True or False) Second graders can use the same scissors they had in first grade.

13. What must first-grade students do to their pencils before bringing them to school?
    a. put their names on them
    b. put them in an art box
    c. sharpen them
    d. both a and c

14. Why must third graders have a school box that is 8" x 5" x 2" in size?

15. Why do students need inexpensive tennis shoes at school for PE?

Eagle Elementary

Extension Activities

1. Look at advertisements that contain school supplies. How much do you think it would cost for a third grader to buy all the supplies needed at Eagle Elementary? Make an estimate using the ads as a guide.
2. Obtain a list of school supplies needed in your classroom or school. Go through your desk and check to see if you have everything you need. Check off the supplies that you have. If some are missing, take the list home so that you will remember which supplies to buy.
3. Where do you go to buy school supplies? Draw a map from your school to the store. Use a map of your city to help you. Include a map key and a compass rose.

Writing Prompts

1. Not all students can afford school supplies. What could you do to help all students at your school get the supplies they need?
2. Choose the three most important items from your classroom supply list. Why are they important? What makes them more important than the rest of the items?
3. Think of an item that is not on your school supply list. Write a letter to your teacher explaining what the item is and why it should be added to the list.

Literature Selections

The Lottie Project by Jacqueline Wilson (Delacorte Press, 1997).

No Copycats Allowed! by Bonnie B. Graves (Hyperion Books for Children, 1998).

Starting School by Johanna Hurwitz (Morrow Junior Books, 1998).

Starting School with an Enemy by Elisa Lynn Carbone (Alfred A. Knopf, 1998).

Warts by Susan Richards Shreve (Tambourine Books, 1996).

Sports Calendar for the Boys and Girls Club

(M) – Main Gym
(A) – Auxiliary Gym

Feb. 1	Feb. 2	Feb. 3	Feb. 4	Feb. 5	Feb. 6	Feb. 7
Free Shoot-Around 6:00 (A)	Boys' Basketball 4:30 (M) Girls' Volleyball 5:30 (A)	Girls' Basketball 5:00 (M) Coed Indoor Soccer 6:30 (A)	Boys' Volleyball 5:00 (M)	Coed Indoor Soccer 6:30 (M)	Boys' Basketball 5:00 (M) Girls' Basketball 7:00 (M)	No Activities Scheduled
Feb. 8	**Feb. 9**	**Feb. 10**	**Feb. 11**	**Feb. 12**	**Feb. 13**	**Feb. 14**
Free Shoot-Around 6:00 (A)	Girls' Basketball 5:00 (M) Free Shoot-Around 6:00 (A)	Girls' Indoor Soccer 5:30 (M) Boys' Basketball 5:00 (A)	No Activities Scheduled	Boys' Basketball 5:00 (M)	Girls' Basketball 10:00 A.M. (M)	Valentine's Day Dance 7:00 (M)
Feb. 15	**Feb. 16**	**Feb. 17**	**Feb. 18**	**Feb. 19**	**Feb. 20**	**Feb. 21**
Girls' Basketball 5:00 (M) Free Shoot-Around 6:00 (A)	Coed Indoor Soccer 6:30 (M) Girls' Volleyball 5:30 (A)	Girls' Basketball 5:00 (M) Boys' Basketball 5:00 (A)	Boys' Basketball 5:00 (M)	Girls' Basketball 5:00 (M)	Girls' Volleyball 10:00 A.M. (M) Boys' Volleyball 5:00 (A)	No Activities Scheduled
Feb. 22	**Feb. 23**	**Feb. 24**	**Feb. 25**	**Feb. 26**	**Feb. 27**	**Feb. 28**
Girls' Basketball 5:00 (M) Free Shoot-Around 6:00 (A)	Boys' Basketball 5:00 (M) Coed Indoor Soccer 6:30 (A)	Boys' Indoor Soccer 6:00 (M)	Girls' Basketball 5:00 (M)	Girls' Volleyball 5:30 (M) Boys' Basketball 5:00 (A)	Girls' Volleyball 10:00 A.M. (M)	No Activities Scheduled

All sports events subject to change due to weather or unexpected occurrences. All times are "P.M." unless otherwise noted.

Boys and Girls Club

Using the sports calendar, answer the questions in complete sentences.

1. What sports are played at this club?

2. What activity is offered at the same time and night every week?

3. How can you tell that there are no athletic events on certain nights?

4. Events may change for what reasons?

5. In which gym does the *(M)* indicate a game is to be played?

6. Why are no athletic events scheduled in the main gym on February 14?

7. Which sport is scheduled for the main gym and which is scheduled for the auxiliary gym on February 10?

8. What is the definition of *coed*?

9. February 7, 14, 21, and 28 are most likely on which day of the week? Explain.

10. Unless otherwise noted, all times shown are during which part of the day?

11. Is there any night with two activities in the same gym? If so, what is the date?

12. Are there more activities for boys or girls (not including shoot-arounds or coed sports)?

13. Why is there only one gym listed on some nights?

14. If you were a member of this Boys and Girls Club, which events would you participate in? Why?

15. How many nights have two events scheduled?

Boys and Girls Club

Use the information from the sports calendar to answer the questions.

1. What sports are played at this club?
   a. basketball   b. volleyball
   c. soccer   d. all of the above

2. (True or False) Boys' basketball is offered at the same time every night that it is offered.

3. On February _____, _____, _____, and _____ there are no activities scheduled.

4. Events might be changed because of
   a. weather
   b. unexpected occurrences
   c. dances
   d. both a and b

5. (True or False) An *(M)* means a sport is to be played in the main gym.

6. Since the _____ is February 14, no sports are scheduled.

7. _____ is played in the main gym, and _____ is in the auxiliary gym on February 10.

8. (True or False) *Coed* is an abbreviation for coeducation, meaning education for both boys and girls .

9. February 7, 14, 21, and 28 are likely on _____ (day of week).

10. (True or False) All times are A.M. unless otherwise noted.

11. On February _____, two games are scheduled for different times in the same gym.

12. Who has more activities they can participate in (not including shoot-arounds or coed sports)?
    a. boys   b. girls
    c. neither   d. men

13. There is only one gym listed on some nights because _____ _____ .

14. If you were a member of this Boys and Girls Club, what events would you participate in? Why?

15. How many nights have two events scheduled?
    a. 8   b. 4
    c. 11   d. 6

Boys and Girls Club

Extension Activities

1. Make a schedule for your daily activities. Be sure to include times. Use the Boys and Girls Club calendar and look for other sample calendars to help you decide which type works best for your schedule.
2. Design your own time word problems. The questions could focus on completing an activity at a certain time when there are other activities to finish first. For example, if you got home at 3:30, had 45 minutes of homework, and had to take a 30-minute walk with the dog, could you play in the soccer game which starts at 4:30?
3. Using the information from the Boys and Girls Club sports calendar, create a new calendar in a different format. For example, you could make a two-column calendar that separates the information for boys' and girls' activities. Or, you could design a calendar that groups information by sport or activity.

Writing Prompts

1. Imagine there are two activities you want to do that are scheduled for the same time and night. What would you do? Explain how and why you made your choice.
2. Why is a calendar like this important for someone who plans the nonathletic events for the Boys and Girls Club? How might she use this calendar to plan concerts or plays?

Literature Selections

About the History of the Calendar by A. E. Evenson (Children's Press, 1972).

Calendars of the World: A Look at Calendars and the Ways We Celebrate by Margo Westrheim (One World Publications, 1993).

Exploring Time by Gillian Chapman and Pam Robson (Millbrook Press, 1995).

The Story of Clocks and Calendars: Marking the Millennium by Betsy Maestro (Lothrop, Lee, & Shepard Books, 1999).

Then and Now: A Book of Days by Starr Ockenga (Houghton Mifflin, 1990).

THE BLUEBIRD

A Delicious Dining Experience

Enjoy our 26-year tradition of fine ingredients and attentive service. All menu items are guaranteed to satisfy. The Bluebird accepts cash and credit cards only. Sorry, no personal checks.

Appetizers

Mozzarella Cheese Sticks 3.95
Potato Soup 2.00
Vegetable Soup 2.00
Potato Skins 3.25
Nachos 3.75
Combination Platter 6.25
(includes any three appetizer choices)

Sandwiches

All sandwiches include your choice of side items—french fries, onion rings, cottage cheese, or applesauce. Add 99¢ to substitute a baked potato. Sandwiches come with your choice of toppings (tomato, lettuce, cheese, and onion).

Hamburger 5.95
a quarter pound of beef
Chicken 5.50
a juicy grilled breast
Chicken Deluxe 6.00
deep-fried and topped with cheese and bacon
Fish 5.75
catfish (deep-fried or broiled)

Salads

Salads include bread sticks or garlic bread.

House Salad 3.20
topped with cheese and croutons
Chicken House Salad 4.20
topped with grilled chicken
Fried Chicken Salad 4.20
topped with fried chicken
Spicy Salad 4.95
topped with spicy grilled chicken or beef

From the Grill

Items ordered from the grill include: a house salad, biscuits or rolls, and two sides. Side items are applesauce, cottage cheese, baked potato, potato soup, vegetable soup, corn, or green beans.

Filet 13.00
10-ounce steak, prepared to your liking
Baby Filet 11.00
6-ounce steak, prepared to your liking
Pork Chops 9.55
two chops—spicy, grilled, or plain
Chicken 8.85
two breasts—covered in barbecue sauce or plain
Sirloin 9.00
10-ounce steak, prepared to your liking

Pasta

Pasta is served with a house salad and your choice of bread sticks or garlic bread.

Spaghetti 6.75
with marinara or meat sauce
Lasagna 8.15
a hearty portion
Magnificent Chicken 7.95
pasta topped with chicken and a light cheese sauce

Children's Menu

These items are for children 12 and under.

Chicken Fingers 2.95
Grilled Cheese 1.95
Hot Dog 1.75
Hamburger 2.25
Turkey Sandwich 2.00

Desserts

All desserts are large enough to share. We recommend 1 dessert for every 2 people.

Ice Cream 3.25
vanilla, chocolate, strawberry, or chocolate chip
(Add 50¢ for topping—chocolate or caramel)
Homemade Pie 3.75
Ask your server for tonight's selection.
Cheesecake 4.00
served with cherry or strawberry topping

The Bluebird

Using the restaurant menu, answer the questions in complete sentences.

1. Which is the most expensive choice in the appetizer section?

2. If you want garlic bread with your meal, you could order from which two sections?

3. Which side items are included in the price of a sandwich?

4. What would it cost to order a grilled chicken sandwich and a baked potato?

5. What are the hamburger toppings?

6. Who can order from the children's menu?

7. How would you find out the different types of pie offered?

8. Six customers at a table want cheesecake. How many pieces should they order?

9. What are good menu choices for someone who likes spicy food?

10. Which is the least expensive meal a fifteen-year-old could order? A ten-year-old?

11. What are the two differences between a filet and a baby filet?

12. Which dish contains cheese sauce, pasta, and chicken?

13. If a customer orders grilled pork chops, how many will she get?

14. Which form of payment is not accepted at The Bluebird?

15. Does The Bluebird seem like a restaurant that you would like? Explain.

Name _____

The Bluebird

Use the information from the restaurant menu to answer the questions.

1. The _____ is the most expensive choice in the appetizer section.

2. If you want garlic bread with your meal, you could order from the _____ or _____ menu sections.

3. (True or False) The price of a sandwich includes french fries, onion rings, cottage cheese, and applesauce.

4. What would it cost to order a grilled chicken sandwich and a baked potato?
   a. $5.50   b. $6.50
   c. $4.51   d. $6.49

5. (True or False) Your choice of toppings is included in the price of a hamburger.

6. Who can order from the children's menu?
   a. a 12-year-old   b. a 2-year-old
   c. a 14-year-old   d. both a and b

7. (True or False) You would look at the menu to find the types of pie offered.

8. Six customers at a table want cheesecake. How many pieces should they order?
   a. 6   b. 12
   c. 4   d. 3

9. For those who like spicy food, some good choices are _____ and _____ .

10. The least expensive meal a fifteen-year-old could order is a _____ . A ten-year-old? _____

11. (True or False) The difference between a filet and baby filet is preparation.

12. Which dish contains cheese sauce, pasta, and chicken?
    a. Chicken Deluxe
    b. Magnificent Chicken
    c. Grilled Chicken
    d. Chicken Fingers

13. If a customer orders grilled pork chops, how many will she get?

14. (True or False) Credit cards are not accepted at The Bluebird.

15. Does The Bluebird seem like a restaurant that you would like? Why or why not?

The Bluebird

Extension Activities

1. Pretend you are opening your own restaurant. What types of food will you serve? Would your restaurant be large or small? Will you have booths or tables? How will you decorate? Think about your options and then design your own restaurant. Your drawings should include foods from the menu, a view from outside the restaurant, and a view from inside.
2. Create an advertisement for your favorite restaurant. It should convince people who have never been there to try it.
3. Research your favorite fast-food restaurant. When did the first one open? What are some of the most popular items on the menu? Why do you think it has been so successful? What makes it your favorite? Present the information to the class.

Writing Prompts

1. Contrast a restaurant you like with one you dislike. Give at least three differences between them.
2. Many people like to eat out. However, some people say that dining out all the time can be unhealthy. Some meals from restaurants are high in fat and do not contain all the vitamins and nutrients that kids need. What is your opinion?

Literature Selections

In Enzo's Splendid Garden by Patricia Polacco (Philomel Books, 1997).

Marge's Diner by Gail Gibbons (T. Y. Crowell, 1989).

Pig-Out Inn by Lois Ruby (Houghton Mifflin, 1987).

The Pizza Mystery by Gertrude Warner (A. Whitman, 1993).

Wrapper Rockets and Trombone Straws: Science at Every Meal
by Edwin J. Sobey (Learning Triangle Press, 1997).

SUPER-DUPER PIZZA

PREPARATION TIME: Dough – 10 minutes, Sauce – 5 minutes, Hamburger – 8 minutes

INGREDIENTS:

Toppings	Dough	Sauce
8 slices of American cheese	3 c. flour	3 cans tomato paste (4 oz.)
1 package of shredded mild cheddar cheese (8 oz.)	1/3 c. vegetable oil	1 can tomato sauce (4 oz.)
4 oz. hamburger	1 tbsp. sugar	1/4 c. sugar
	1 tbsp. salt	

TO MAKE DOUGH:

Mix flour and oil together in large bowl until mixture has moist texture. Slowly add sugar and then salt. Mix completely. Make sure dough is not bumpy.

TO MAKE SAUCE:

Empty contents of each can into large mixing bowl. Blend with spoon or beater. Stir in sugar. Mix completely. Keep refrigerated until ready to use.

Hamburger preparation: Brown 4 oz. hamburger over low heat in large skillet.

COOKING DIRECTIONS:

1. Preheat oven to 375 degrees.
2. Carefully flatten dough on a greased cookie sheet. Make sure dough thickness is even.
3. Spread sauce evenly over dough. Leave about 1/2 inch of outside edge free of sauce for crust.
4. Sprinkle hamburger evenly over layer of sauce.
5. Cut American cheese slices into 1/4-inch-wide strips and spread over hamburger. Sprinkle cheddar cheese over all layers.
6. Place cookie sheet in oven and bake for 27 minutes or until crust turns light brown.

Makes 4 servings.

Nutrition information: Serving size – 1 slice; Calories – 250; Fat – 9g; Carbohydrates – 10g; Protein – 6g

VEGGIE DELIGHT PIZZA (see recipe opposite page)

Super-Duper Pizza

Using the recipe, answer the questions in complete sentences.

1. How many slices of American cheese are needed for this recipe?

2. What is the first thing you must do after the dough, sauce, and hamburger are ready?

3. What are the sauce ingredients?

4. How many calories are in two pizza slices?

5. Which kind of heat is needed to brown the hamburger?

6. What has the longest preparation time?

7. Why should the dough thickness be even?

8. If you opened two 8-ounce cans of tomato paste, how much would you have left after making the sauce?

9. What size package of cheddar cheese will you need?

10. Which ingredient uses the most sugar?

11. What is the difference between this recipe's bake time and preparation time?

12. Before you put the American cheese on the pizza, what must you do to it?

13. If you ate the whole pizza by yourself, how many grams of carbohydrates would you eat?

14. How much pizza should be left without sauce on the dough's outside edge?

15. What is the first step to make the dough?

Super-Duper Pizza

Use the information from the recipe to answer the questions.

1. How many slices of American cheese are needed for this recipe?
   a. 2   b. 6
   c. 10   d. 8

2. After getting the hamburger, dough, and sauce ready, you must _____ the oven.

3. List the sauce ingredients.

4. _____ calories are in two pizza slices.
   a. 500   b. 250
   c. 375   d. 750

5. (True or False) When browning the hamburger, use low heat.

6. The _____ has the longest preparation time.

7. (True or False) It doesn't matter if the dough is spread out evenly or not.

8. (True or False) You would have four ounces of tomato paste left if you opened two 8-ounce cans.

9. How much cheddar cheese does the recipe require?
   a. 8 slices   b. 8 ounces
   c. 4 ounces   d. 2 cups

10. (True or False) The dough gets more sugar than the sauce.

11. (True or False) The total preparation time is longer than the bake time.

12. What must you do right before putting the American cheese on the pizza?
    a. Spread sauce evenly over the dough.
    b. Place the cookie sheet into the oven.
    c. Sprinkle on the hamburger.
    d. Put cheddar cheese on the dough.

13. If you ate the whole pizza yourself, you ate how many grams of carbohydrates?
    a. 40   b. 30
    c. 20   d. 10

14. You leave _____ an inch around the outside of the pizza to form the crust.

15. Write the first thing you do when making the dough.

Super-Duper Pizza

Extension Activities

1. Bring in some of your family's favorite recipes. Construct a classroom cookbook with your friends and present it to your teacher.
2. The next time an adult cooks in your home, ask if you can watch or help. Look at the various sizes of measuring cups used. Notice how much of each ingredient is used for the recipe.
3. Ask your teacher about having a baked goods day. With adult supervision, you and your classmates can prepare your favorite baked snacks at home and bring them in to share. Each of you can bring in a copy of the recipe and share what ingredients you used. Then, you can sample the tasty treats together.

Writing Prompts

1. Do you know someone who is a good cook? Does that person use recipes? Why do you think he cooks well?
2. Write a letter to the chef of your favorite restaurant. Ask her what kind of education and experience it took to become a successful chef.
3. Make up a recipe using some of the basic food ingredients that you like. Look at sample recipes from cookbooks for ideas. List the ingredients, instructions, preparation time, cooking time, and nutrition information. With adult help, prepare your new recipe to see if you have created a yummy new dish.

Literature Selections

Heat Wave by Helen Ketteman (Walker and Co., 1998).

Home Cooking Sampler: Family Favorites from A to Z by Peggy K. Glass (Prentice Hall, 1988).

Justin and the Best Biscuits in the World by Dian Thomas (Lothrop, Lee, & Shepard, 1986).

Oregon Trail Cooking by Mary Gunderson (Blue Earth Books, 2000).

Roughing It Easy by Dian Thomas (The Dian Thomas Company, 1997).

It's a Party!

What: Ian's Birthday Party

When: Saturday, May 2

Where: Forest Dale Park

What to bring: Nothing! Just come and be prepared to have fun!

How to get there: That depends where you're coming from. (See directions.)

Directions

From Kent St. – This street leads to the back entrance of the park. You will enter the park and pass by the road leading to the other entrance (it will be on the right). Once you pass that road, we will be the third pavilion on the right (#7). Look for a sign that reads "Ian's Party."

From Garfield St. – Stay on Garfield until it ends. Take a right onto Rockford St. The first left will be Kent St. Then, follow the Kent St. directions above.

From North River Rd. – Drive south on North River until you see Brighton Rd. Take a right onto Brighton Rd. This will take you to the park entrance. Turn left into the park at the stop sign. Then, continue with the directions below.*

From Hillside Dr. – Stay on Hillside until it curves to the right and turns into Houston Ave. Stay on Houston Ave. until you come to a stoplight at Spring Park Rd. Go straight, and you will be on Brighton Rd. This will take you to the park entrance. At the stop sign, turn left into the park. Then, continue with the directions below.*

*There is only one road in the park (called Park Roadway). From the entrance, follow the road until you come to a stop sign. Take a right at the stop sign. We will be the third pavilion on the right (#7). Look for a sign that reads "Ian's Party."

Sailing Along to a Happy Birthday!

8 years old

Ian's Birthday

Using the party invitation, answer the questions in complete sentences.

1. This invitation announces what event?

2. If driving from Garfield Street, how long would you stay on that street?

3. What is the one road in the park?

4. Hillside Drive turns into what street?

5. How do you get to Ian's party?

6. Which street leads to the park's back entrance?

7. At what park is the party taking place?

8. At what sign must you turn left when entering the park from Brighton Road?

9. On what road is the park's front entrance?

10. At what pavilion is this event being held? How will you know you are at the right one?

11. You must travel on what street before turning onto Rockford Street?

12. How many different entrances to the park are there?

13. What street turns into Brighton Road at a stoplight?

14. What would be a reason to have the party at a park?

15. Are the party directions clear? Give two reasons to support your answer.

Name _____

Ian's Birthday

Use the information from the party invitation to answer the questions.

1. This invitation is for _____
    _____ .

2. (True or False) If driving from Garfield
    Street, stay on it until the street ends.

3. What is the name of the road in the park?
    a. Forest Dale Park   b. Park Roadway
    c. Spring Road   d. Hillside Drive

4. Hillside Drive turns into _____
    _____.

5. According to the invitation, how do you
    get to the party?

6. The street that leads to the back
    entrance of the park is _____
    _____ .

7. _____ Park
    is the location for this event.

8. At what sign must you turn left when
    entering the park from Brighton Road?

9. (True or False) One of the entrances to
    the park is on Brighton Road.

10. How will you know where pavilion #7 is?
    a. It will be on the left.
    b. A sign will read "Ian's Party."
    c. both a and b
    d. none of the above

11. Before turning onto Rockford Street, you
    must travel on which street?
    a. Kent Street   b. Garfield Street
    c. Brighton Road   d. North Road

12. There are _____ different entrances to
    the park.

13. (True or False) Spring Park Road turns
    into Brighton Road at a stop sign.

14. What would be a reason to have the
    party at a park?

15. Do you think the directions are clear?
    Support your answer with two reasons.

Ian's Birthday

Extension Activities

1. Write directions to your home from two different locations (for example: from school and from a local park). Then, draw two different maps. Each one should show how to get there from one location. Provide written directions on your maps in places where details could be misread.
2. Locate a street map and a written set of directions to a destination. Using the directions, track your way through the street map to see if you can find the destination.
3. Research how different cultures celebrate birthdays. Write a short report to present to friends, family, or classmates.

Writing Prompts

1. Write a thank-you letter to someone who gave you a birthday or other gift. Be sure to tell the person what you liked about the gift. Be specific about why you enjoyed it.
2. Create an invitation to a birthday party. Be sure to include the information that your friends would need to know. Use Ian's party invitation as an example.
3. How do directions help make it easier for people to get from place to place? How do people, such as bus drivers, get from place to place without directions?

Literature Selections

Birthday Poems: A Celebration edited by Jason Shinder (Thunder's Mouth Press, 2002).

Hannah's Journal: The Story of an Immigrant Girl by Marissa Moss (Silver Whistle/Harcourt, 2000).

How Maps Are Made by Martyn Bramwell (Lerner Publishing Group, 1998).

It's Justin Time, Amber Brown by Paula Danzinger (G. P. Putnam's Sons, 2001).

Mapping Our World by Martyn Bramwell (Lerner Publishing Group, 1998).

CD-0581 • Real-World Reading Comprehension

Dear Students and Parents,

U. R. Smart Elementary School has an exciting year of extracurricular activities planned for students! Below you will find a schedule of clubs and activities. This list should help students decide what activities to sign up for this year. Starting and ending months, days of the week, and activity times are given. (Some of the activities may require time or date changes due to student participation or scheduling conflicts.) All activities are voluntary. Each teacher sponsor will send home additional information as the start-up date nears. Watch the school newsletter for more information. Morning (A.M.) activities will take place 30 minutes before school. Afternoon (P.M.) activities will begin at 3:15.

ACTIVITY	GRADE(S)	MONTHS	DAY(S)	TIME	SPONSOR(S)
Yearbook	4th	Sept.–May	2nd Thurs. of month	A.M.	Smith/Crawford
Student Council	4th	Sept.–May	1st Thurs. of month	A.M.	Anderson/Phillips
Earth Savers	4th	Oct.–May	1st Tues. of month	A.M.	Phillips
Spelling Bowl	4th	Sept.–Nov.	Mon. & Wed.	A.M.	Vanderbilt
Choir	3rd/4th	Sept.–May	Thursday	A.M.	Morris
Wee Ensemble	4th	Sept.–May	Friday	A.M.	Morris
Drama	2nd	Jan.–Feb.	Tues. & Thurs.	P.M.	Meadow/Matlock
	3rd/4th	Sept.–Dec.	Tues. & Thurs.	P.M.	Mason/Garrett
Dance Club	3rd	Sept.–May	Tuesday	A.M.	Johnson
	4th	Sept.–May	Wednesday	A.M.	Johnson
Math Bowl	4th	Oct.–March	Tuesday	P.M.	Thomas
Track	4th	April–May	2-3 times per week	P.M.	Johnson
Service Club	3rd/4th	Sept.–May	2nd Wed. of month	P.M.	Adams/Anderson
Fall Fling Club	K-4	Sept.–Dec.	Wednesday	P.M.	Johnson
Winter Club	K-4	Jan.–Feb.	Friday	P.M.	Johnson
Spring Sports	K-4	March–May	Wednesday	P.M.	Johnson

U. R. Smart Elementary

Using the activity schedule, answer the questions in complete sentences.

1. How many extracurricular activities are offered at this school?

2. During what months does Spelling Bowl meet?

3. If you are a third grader, how many activities are available to you?

4. How many activities can first graders join?

5. When does Student Council meet?

6. Could a student participate in both Student Council and Choir? Explain.

7. Who will be sending out more information about Math Bowl?

8. What time do all P.M. activities begin?

9. What activities only meet on Fridays?

10. Who sponsors the most activities?

11. Who are the sponsors for Drama Club?

12. What months, days, and times does Yearbook meet?

13. How many days a week does Track meet?

14. Which of these activities would you like to join? Why?

15. Do you think it is important for students to participate in extracurricular activities? Why or why not?

U. R. Smart Elementary

Use the information from the activity schedule to answer the questions.

1. _____ extracurricular activities are offered.
   a. Fourteen   b. Seventeen
   c. Sixteen   d. Twenty

2. (True or False) Spelling Bowl meets in only October and November.

3. If you are in third grade, how many activities are available to you?
   a. 7   b. 4
   c. 3   d. 10

4. (True or False) First graders are not eligible to join any activities.

5. When does Student Council meet?
   a. Sept.-May, 1st Thurs. of month, P.M.
   b. Oct.-May, 2nd Thurs. of month, A.M.
   c. Sept.-April, 3rd Thurs. of month, P.M.
   d. Sept.-May, 1st Thurs. of month, A.M.

6. Can a student participate in both Student Council and Choir? Why or why not?

7. _____ will send more information about Math Bowl.

8. (True or False) All P.M. activities begin about 3:45.

9. _____ and _____ both meet on Fridays.

10. Which teacher sponsors the most activities?
    a. Thomas   b. Morris
    c. Johnson   d. Phillips

11. Who are the sponsors for Drama Club?
    a. Mason/Garrett
    b. Mason/Garrett, Meadow/Matlock
    c. Mason
    d. Meadow/Matlock

12. When does Yearbook meet?
    a. Sept.-Dec., last Tues. of month, P.M.
    b. Sept.-April, Tues., A.M.
    c. Sept.-May, 3rd Thurs. of month, A.M.
    d. Sept.-May, 2nd Thurs. of month, A.M.

13. Track meets _____ times per week.

14. Which of these activities would you like to join? Why?

15. Do you think it is important for students to participate in extracurricular activities? Why or why not?

U. R. Smart Elementary

Extension Activities

1. Pretend that you are running for Student Council. You want to convince other students that you would be an excellent representative. Create a poster to encourage your classmates to vote for you.
2. Survey your classmates to find out how many extracurricular activities they are involved in. Create a bar graph to display the results.
3. Service Club is a group that participates in projects that help others. Try to think of a service project you and your classmates could complete. Could you pick up litter on the playground? Could you help a teacher by working with students in a lower grade? Decide on a project you would like to do, create a plan to accomplish it, and complete it.

Writing Prompts

1. Many people believe children should be involved in extracurricular activities. They think that children are less likely to get into trouble if they have something to do after school. Other people feel that children don't need to participate in planned activities and should spend more time at play. What is your opinion?
2. If you could choose only one extracurricular activity to participate in, what would it be? Give at least three reasons why you would choose this activity over all others.

Literature Selections

The Animal Rescue Club by John Himmelman (HarperCollins Children's Books, 1998).

Baseball Saved Us by Ken Mochizuki (Lee & Low Books, 1993).

Class President by Johanna Hurwitz (Morrow Junior Books, 1990).

Life on a Pig Farm by Judy Wolfman (Lerner Publishing Group, 2001).

On Guard by Donna Jo Napoli (Dutton, 1997).

The Young Track and Field Athlete by Colin Jackson (Dorling Kindersley, 1996).

PLAYGROUND RULES

1. All students will go to recess unless they have a parent/guardian's note to explain why they cannot participate. For longer periods of time (more than 3 days), a doctor's note will be needed.
2. Students should bring their coats and playground materials. Students without appropriate clothes for the weather will go to study hall for the entire recess.
3. Students will enter and exit the school building in an orderly manner with quiet voices.
4. Students are responsible for returning items taken out at recess.
5. Recess is limited to selected areas away from the school building. Students should not play near the school building.
6. Standing on or jumping from swings is not allowed. Students should maintain a safe distance when walking behind or in front of swings.
7. Students must go down slides feet first with one person on the slide at a time. Do not climb up the slides.
8. **No wrestling, tripping, or fighting** will be allowed.
9. Two-hand touch football is allowed. There should be no other contact—**no tackling**.
10. In case of severe weather, recess will be held in certain areas inside the building (usually in designated classrooms).
11. If certain areas of the playground cannot be used due to special activities or other unforeseen circumstances, students will be permitted to play on blacktop areas only.

Consequences

First violations will result in a warning by the school employee in charge of recess.

Second violations will result in a loss of recess time. Amount of time will be determined by the school employee.

Third violations will result in a trip to the principal's office and a note sent to student's parents.

Four or more violations will result in a trip to the principal's office, a call to parents, and a suspension from recess.

Severe violations will be treated as a fourth violation.

BUSY BEE ELEMENTARY ⚙ SCHOOL PROPERTY

Busy Bee Elementary

Using the playground rules, answer the questions in complete sentences.

1. What happens the first time someone gets in trouble at recess?

2. Can students play football?

3. In severe weather, where is recess held?

4. List the three events that happen when a student gets in trouble four or more times on the playground.

5. All students have to go to recess unless they have what?

6. Where will students be able to play if the playground is too wet?

7. Why is #7 a playground rule?

8. If students play football, what can they not do?

9. How will a severe problem at recess be treated?

10. A doctor's note is needed if a student is going to do what?

11. List the three things that are not allowed on the playground at any time.

12. What are the two things students who are swinging cannot do?

13. How would parents find out their child got in trouble at recess a third time?

14. If a student takes a basketball out to recess, who makes sure the basketball is brought back into the school building?

15. On cold days, where will students who didn't bring coats go?

Busy Bee Elementary

Use the information from the playground rules to answer the questions.

1. A first violation results in a/an _____ .
   a. note home   b. office referral
   c. warning   d. loss of recess

2. (True or False) Students are allowed to play two-hand touch football.

3. If the weather is bad, recess will be in
   a. the gym   b. classrooms
   c. the cafeteria   d. the library

4. If a student gets in trouble four times, he is sent to the office, his parents are called, and he is _____ .

5. Students with a _____ do not have to go to recess.

6. (True or False) Students will play on the blacktop if the playground is too wet.

7. Why is rule #7 a playground rule?

8. If playing football, students cannot _____ .
   a. tackle   b. pass
   c. block   d. kick the ball

9. A severe problem will be treated as a _____ violation.
   a. 1st   b. 2nd
   c. 3rd   d. 4th

10. A doctor's note is needed if a student is going to miss _____ days of recess.

11. List the three things that are not allowed on the playground at any time.

12. Students cannot _____ on or _____ from the swings.

13. How would parents find out their child got in trouble for the third time?
    a. a phone call   b. a note home
    c. an E-mail   d. their child

14. _____ are responsible for returning items taken out at recess.

15. A student who has not brought a coat on a cold day must go to
    a. the office   b. the gym
    c. study hall   d. the library

Busy Bee Elementary

Extension Activities

1. Design your own school playground. Then, write a list of rules for the playground. List the consequences for breaking your playground rules.
2. Talk to a friend about the importance of playground rules. Why do you and your friend think that certain things are allowed and other things are not? Find out what things you agree upon and what things you feel differently about.
3. Draw a design for a new piece of playground equipment. Write a paragraph explaining what makes it a unique piece of equipment. Write a list of playground rules specific to your creation to make sure students use it safely.

Writing Prompts

1. Write a persuasive letter to the principal asking for a rule to be added or changed. Include at least three reasons why this rule should be added or changed.
2. Why is safety on the playground important? How could your school's playground be made safer to play on?
3. What is your favorite recess activity? Describe the activity in detail and explain why it is your favorite.

Literature Selections

A Kid's Guide to Staying Safe at Playgrounds by Maribeth Boelts (PowerKids Press, 1997).

Mary Anne and the Playground Fight by Ann Martin (Scholastic, 1998).

Peace on the Playground: Nonviolent Ways of Problem-Solving by Eileen Lucas (F. Watts, 1991).

Playing on the Playground by Dorothy Chlad (Children's Press, 1987).

Safety on the Playground by Lucia Raatma (Bridgestone Books, 1999).

Fun○**ville**

Summer   Sports Camp

For summer fun,
run with the Buffalo

Why: To increase athletic skill and knowledge

Who: Boys and girls in 3rd and 4th grades (Qualified coaches & staff will instruct campers.)

What: A sports camp hosted by Funville High School Athletic Department Camps are held for basketball, baseball, softball, flag football, contact football, and cheerleading. Cost is $100.00 per session plus the nonrefundable deposit* (due on the first day of camp).

When: Choose from the sessions listed below. Each session lasts five days, from 8:00 A.M. to 5:30 P.M. Lunch is provided each day.

All sports will be offered during each session.

1st session	June 7–11	4th session	June 28–July 2
2nd session	June 14–18	5th session	July 5–9
3rd session	June 21–25	6th session	July 12–16

Where: Sports Camp will be held in the Funville Sports Complex. Campers will be separated by sport.

How: Fill out the application below and send it to the Funville High School Athletic Department with the onetime nonrefundable deposit* of $20.00.

-------------------------------- Cut and return application below -------------------------------

Name _____ Grade ____ School _____

Parent's Name _____ Phone _____

Session Number ___ Sport _____

Medical Condition(s) _____

Family Doctor _____ Phone _____

Emergency Contact _____ Phone _____

NOTE: Each camper must have a physical on file before the first day of camp.

Questions???
Call Steve Fuller at 555-1212.

Funville Sports Camp

Using the application, answer the questions in complete sentences.

1. What sports are offered at this camp?

2. Who can attend Funville Sports Camp?

3. What session number would you sign up for if you want to attend sports camp from June 28-July 2?

4. How many days does one session last?

5. If you have additional questions about camp, what should you do?

6. If you want to attend two sessions of sports camp, how much will it cost?

7. How much is the deposit that you must send with your sports camp application?

8. What is one thing each camper must have before the first day of camp?

9. Where is Funville Sports Camp held?

10. Jason registered for baseball during session 2 at camp. Dion registered for basketball during session 2. Will the boys be in the same group?

11. Pedro wants to go to sports camp, but his family will be gone on vacation from June 1-20. He will be leaving again from July 1-July 13. Is there a session he can attend? If so, which one?

12. Who will be working with the campers?

13. To whom should you send your sports camp application and deposit?

14. What time should campers be picked up?

15. What are some reasons kids may want to go to sports camp?

Funville Sports Camp

Use the information from the application to answer the questions.

1. List the sports offered at this camp.

2. Who can attend this camp?
   a. boys in 3rd and 4th grades
   b. boys in 4th grade
   c. girls in 3rd grade
   d. boys and girls in 3rd and 4th grades

3. (True or False) You would register for session 4 to attend from June 28 –July 2.

4. How long does one session last?
   a. a week   b. a day
   c. 5 days   d. July 7–11

5. If you have questions about sports camp, you should _____ .

6. The cost of two sessions of camp is
   a. $320.00   b. $220.00
   c. $100.00   d. $150.00

7. (True or False) The deposit that you must send with your application is $20.

8. Campers must ____ before the first day.
   a. practice   b. sleep
   c. get a physical   d. buy equipment

9. This camp will be held at the _____ .
   a. high school   b. sports complex
   c. local gym   d. hospital

10. (True or False) For session 2, Jason registered for baseball, and Dion registered for basketball. The two boys will be in the same group at camp.

11. Pedro would like to go to sports camp, but from June 1–20, he will be on vacation. Then, he will be leaving again from July 1–13. Is there a session he can attend? _____ Which one? _____

12. Who will be working with the campers?
   a. teachers   b. coaches and staff
   c. sports stars   d. both a and b

13. (True or False) You should send your application and deposit to the Funville High School Athletic Department.

14. Campers need to be picked up at
   a. 5:30 P.M.   b. 5:30 A.M.
   c. 8:00 A.M.   d. 8:00 P.M.

15. What are some reasons kids may want to go to sports camp?

Funville Sports Camp

Extension Activities

1. Interview a friend who has been to camp recently. Before the interview, write a list of questions to ask. For example: What kind of a camp did you attend? What were the best parts of camp? What were the worst parts? Would you return to this camp?
2. If you could run your own camp, what kind of camp would it be? What are some activities you would have for your campers? Write a short paragraph to answer these questions. Then, draw a picture of what your camp would look like, showing the activities your camp would offer.
3. Use your picture and paragraph from #2 to create a full-page ad to encourage kids to come to your new camp.

Writing Prompts

1. Pretend you have been at summer camp for a month. Write a letter to your parents telling them what you've been doing and how you're feeling.
2. Would you want to go to Funville Sports Camp? Why or why not? Give at least three reasons for your answer.
3. Of all sports, which promotes the healthiest benefits? Support your opinion with three strong reasons.

Literature Selections

Ernestine and Amanda: Summer Camp Ready or Not!
by Sandra Belton (Simon and Schuster Books for Young Readers, 1997).

The Great Summer Camp Catastrophe
by Jean Van Leeuwen (Dial Books for Young Readers, 1992).

Miami Makes the Play by Patricia McKissack (Golden Book Publishers, 2001).

Shot From Midfield by Tommy Hallowell (Viking, 1990).

Werewolves Don't Go to Summer Camp by Debbie Dadey (Scholastic, 1991).

PERMISSION FORM FOR DINOSAUREUM FIELD TRIP

(Due back to Mrs. Morgan by October 31.)

Date: Thursday, November 11

Cost: $5.00 per student, $8.00 per chaperone

What to bring: a backpack and disposable sack lunch (No electronic devices!)

Depart from school: 8:30 A.M.   **Return to school:** 3:30 P.M.

— — — — — — — — — — — — — — Cut and return bottom of permission form. — — — — — — — — — — — —

I give my consent for _____ to go on this trip.
                                    (student's name)

_____
(parent/guardian's signature)

In case of emergency, I (parent/guardian) can be contacted at _____ .
                                                              (phone number)

If I cannot be reached, please contact _____
at _____ .   (name/relationship to student)
       (phone number)

Family Doctor (name and phone number) _____

Family Dentist (name and phone number)_____

•••

I would like to be a chaperone* for the museum field trip on November 11.

_____
(parent/guardian's signature)

*If you do not have a background check on file with the district, it must be completed and approved before chaperoning the field trip. This process takes about three weeks.

Dinosaureum Field Trip

Using the permission form, answer the questions in complete sentences.

1. When is this field trip?

2. When do the people going on the field trip leave from the school?

3. What is a chaperone?

4. What information is required about the family doctor?

5. What should students bring with them?

6. If a parent wants to be a chaperone but has not met the condition listed on the permission form, what must she do?

7. Why does the form request information about a doctor and dentist?

8. Why do you think it costs more for a chaperone to go on the trip?

9. At what time will the students arrive back at school from the field trip?

10. Why is a second emergency contact person needed?

11. What information is needed about the person in #10?

12. What should students not bring?

13. Do you think a student going on this field trip should bring spending money?

14. How long does it take to process a background check?

15. How many times would a parent/guardian have to sign the permission form if he wanted to be a chaperone?

Dinosaureum Field Trip

Use the information from the permission form to answer the questions.

1. What is the date of this field trip?
   a. October 31   b. November 11
   c. October 11   d. December 31

2. (True or False) Those going on the field trip will leave the school at 8:30 P.M.

3. (True or False) A chaperone is always a teacher.

4. The doctor's _____ and _____ are required.

5. What should students bring with them?
   a. a backpack   b. a sack lunch
   c. both a and b   d. a chaperone

6. If an adult does not have a background check and wants to chaperone, she must get one completed and _____ .

7. Why does the form ask for information about a doctor and dentist?

8. (True or False) It costs more money for a chaperone to go on the trip.

9. Students will return to school at _____ .

10. Why are two emergency contact people required?

11. The information needed for the second emergency person includes _____ _____ .

12. What can students not bring with them?
    a. a backpack
    b. a sack lunch
    c. an electronic device
    d. all of the above

13. Do you think a student going on this field trip should bring spending money?

14. (True or False) It takes two weeks to process a background check.

15. The parent/guardian would have to sign the form a total of _____ times if he wanted to be a chaperone.

Dinosaureum Field Trip

Extension Activities

1. Create your own miniature museum exhibit about a specific topic that you like. Collect items and information about that topic to share. Store the museum items in a box or other container. Encourage a friend to make one too, so that you can "visit" each other's museum exhibits.
2. Design a museum floor plan for your exhibit from #1. Indicate how the exhibit would be shown, such as its location, display setup, and lighting.
3. Research and calculate how much it costs to go on a field trip, including admission, food, transportation, etc.

Writing Prompts

1. After your next field trip, write a thank-you letter to the person in charge of the place you visited. Tell her about your favorite part of the experience.
2. Think of a place you think would be beneficial to visit for a class field trip and write a proposal to your teacher outlining the reasons why that place should be chosen for the next field trip.
3. Why is it necessary for schools to send out permission forms for field trips? In your opinion, are these forms necessary? Why or why not?

Literature Selections

Friendship across Arctic Waters: Alaskan Cub Scouts Visit Their Soviet Neighbors
by Claire Rudolf Murphy (Dutton Children's Books, 1991).

Herbie Jones by Suzy Kline (G. P. Putnam's Sons, 1985).

I Gave Thomas Edison My Sandwich by Floyd Moore (A. Whitman, 1995).

Time Train by Paul Fleischman (HarperCollins Children's Books, 1991).

Ultimate Field Trip 1: Adventures in the Amazon Rain Forest
by Susan Goodman (Aladdin Paperbacks, 1995).

Mr. Boxley

"CLASS PICNIC"

CLASS, ISN'T THIS A GREAT SPOT FOR OUR PICNIC?

YEAH!

THIS IS COOL!

LOOK AT THE WOODS OVER THERE!

I BET THERE ARE SOME GREAT TRAILS TO HIKE AROUND HERE!

WE FOUND A GREAT PLACE TO GO SWIMMING!

I JUST WANT TO DIG INTO THE GREAT FOOD WE BROUGHT ALONG.

UH-OH!

WHAT?

I GUESS WE'RE NOT THE ONLY ONES WHO THINK THIS PICNIC IS GREAT!

YIKES!

THIS BUGS ME!

Ms. Buggy The Ant Teacher

Class, isn't this a great spot for our class picnic?

Yeah!

This is cool!

Look at all those picnic baskets over there.

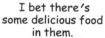

I bet there's some delicious food in them.

We're gonna go explore!

I can't wait to dig into all the great food!

Uh-Oh.

What?

I guess we're not the only ones who can't wait to dig in!

Head for the hill!

Jazzville Journal

Using the comic strips, answer the questions in complete sentences.

1. At first, how do the students in both classes feel about their picnics?

2. How is Ms. Buggy's class picnic ruined?

3. Name three things that Mr. Boxley's class would like to do on their picnic.

4. What is the main activity Ms. Buggy's class wants to do?

5. Two ants say, "We're gonna go explore!" What's unusual about the word *gonna*?

6. The two classes see their picnics from different points of view. What is meant by the term *point of view*?

7. In the last frame, what look does Mr. Boxley have on his face? Why?

8. How is Mr. Boxley's class picnic ruined?

9. What does Mr. Boxley mean when he says, "I guess we're not the only ones who think this picnic is great!"

10. How do pictures explain the meaning of comic strips? Would you understand these comic strips if there were no pictures?

11. What do you predict will happen after the last scene in the second comic strip?

12. Of the two comic strips, which one could not happen in real life?

13. Do the ants or the humans deserve the food in the picnic baskets? Why?

14. How do you think Ms. Buggy feels about the humans? Why?

15. Does the picnic site in the comic strips look like a place you would like to picnic? Why or why not?

Name _____

Jazzville Journal

Use the information from the comic strips to answer the questions.

1. At first, both of the classes are
   a. excited   b. disappointed
   c. bored   d. upset

2. Ms. Buggy's picnic is ruined when humans
   a. eat the food   b. show up
   c. go hiking   d. both a and c

3. Mr. Boxley's class wants to _____, _____, and _____ .

4. The main activity Ms. Buggy's class wants to do is _____ .

5. Two ants say, "We're gonna go explore!" What does *gonna* mean?

6. The two classes see the picnic from different points of view. That means:
   a. the way you see a certain situation
   b. where someone is resting
   c. looking at something in the distance
   d. both a and b

7. (True or False) In the last frame, Mr. Boxley looks happy.

8. Mr. Boxley's picnic is ruined when ants
   a. go hiking   b. talk to him
   c. cover the food   d. go swimming

9. (True or False) When Mr. Boxley says, "I guess we're not the only ones who think this picnic is great!" he is talking about his students having a good time.

10. (True or False) Pictures in comic strips make them easier to understand.

11. What do you predict will happen after the last scene in the second comic strip?

12. Which comic strip could not happen in real life?
    a. Mr. Boxley's class picnic
    b. Ms. Buggy's class picnic
    c. both a and b
    d. neither a nor b

13. Who do you think deserves the food in the picnic baskets? Why?

14. (True or False) Ms. Buggy does not like the humans being at her class picnic.

15. Does the picnic site in the comic strip look like a place you would like to picnic? Why or why not?

Jazzville Journal

Extension Activities

1. Use six boxes to draw your own set of pictures for Mr. Boxley's class picnic or Ms. Buggy's class picnic. Do not include any words. Cut the six pictures apart. Give them to a friend and see if he can put the pictures in the correct order.
2. Create your own comic strip. Use characters of your own or characters such as Mr. Boxley and Ms. Buggy to help you get started.
3. Cut out several comic strips from newspapers. Glue them to a large piece of poster board to make a collage of the ones you think are the funniest.

Writing Prompts

1. Describe what you think would be the perfect setting for a picnic. What would it look like? Try to include all five senses in your description.
2. Write two paragraphs comparing and contrasting the human picnic with the ant picnic. Your first paragraph should explain how the two picnics were the same. Your second paragraph should tell how the two picnics were different.
3. Do you think the two comic strips were funny? Why or why not?

Literature Selections

The Art of Making Comic Books by Michael Pellowski (Lerner Publishing Group, 1995).

The Berenstain Bears and the Great Ant Attack by Stan Berenstain (Random House, 2000).

Cartoonists by Bradley Steffens and Robyn Weaver (Lucent Books, 2000).

Cartoons and Cartooning by Harvey Weiss (Houghton Mifflin, 1990).

Funny Papers: Behind the Scenes of the Comic by Elaine Scott (Morrow Junior Books, 1993).

The Third Garfield Treasury by Jim Davis (Ballentine Books, 1985).

The True Story of the Three Little Pigs by John Scieszka (Viking, 1989).

Answer Key—Open-Ended Format

Page 6: Honesty Pays

1. Anne Longlunger wrote this article.
2. The name of the newspaper is The Ridgeville Review.
3. The title of the article is "Honesty Pays."
4. The article is mainly about Alice Sampson.
5. The events took place in Ridgeville, Indiana.
6. The article was printed on December 22, 2002.
7. The events of the article took place two weeks ago.
8. Alice found more than $2,000.
9. Alice found the wallet under a clothing rack in a store.
10. Alice returned the wallet to the store office.
11. Albert Humphries gave Alice $100 and set up a fund for her college education.
12.–15. Answers will vary.

Page 10: Washington Elementary

1. The lunch menu is for December.
2. No lunch is served on December 10.
3. Classes resume on January 6.
4. You can find the answer to the grains food group question under the snowflakes.
5. You should eat 2–3 servings daily from the meat/protein and dairy groups.
6. December 10 is a half day for students and no lunch is served.
7. The two side items for December 12 are macaroni & cheese and green beans.
8. There are no lunch choices for December 7, 8, 14, or 15 because these are weekend days.
9. School closes for Winter Break after classes on December 18.
10. Potatoes are the vegetable that is served most often in side dishes.
11. Beef burritos are served on December 3.
12. Ten days offer a fruit.
13. Pepperoni is part of the meat/protein group.
14. A salad is served as a side item on December 4, 13, and 18.
15. Answers will vary.

Page 14: Exploring the Universe

1. The name of the game is Exploring the Universe.
2. Two to eight people can play.
3. The materials include a game board, 1 die, answer key, storage box, 60 Challenge Cards, 8 game pieces, 60 Asteroid Cards, and the game rule sheet.
4. For a player to arrive back on Earth, he must have an exact roll of the die.
5. The youngest player goes first.
6. You pick a Challenge Card when you land on an Asteroid Box.
7. Game pieces are placed at the Space Station.
8. If an incorrect answer is given, the Answer Key Keeper can have one player follow the directions on an Asteroid Card.
9. Answers will vary.
10. The optional rule is that Challenge Cards can be read aloud or silently.
11. Answers will vary.
12. The game ends when someone lands on Earth.
13. The first person to reach Earth wins.
14. Answers will vary.
15. A missing storage box would not affect the play of the game.

Page 18: Get-Up-Early Specials

1. The sale is on Saturday.
2. Answers will vary.
3. The 66% off items are kids' jackets and coats and girls' tops and skirts.
4. The Gentry train sets are at the season's lowest price.
5. The regular price of tees is $34.
6. The three main categories of sale items are fashion, toys, and electronics.
7. Scooter prices were reduced twice.
8. Rugged Racer, Cool BMX, and Zapitron are on sale.
9. The total percentage saved on bike helmets is 60%.
10. The sale lasts for two hours.
11. The 13" color TV is regularly $250 and is on sale for $124.99.
12. Answers will vary.
13. Three items could have regular prices over $200 (bikes, 13" color TVs, CD players).
14. You could save the largest dollar amount on a 13" color TV.
15. Leather jackets and bikes share sales price and could share regular price.

Page 22: Eagle Elementary

1. There are five grades in this school.
2. No, the students won't receive all the supplies when they pay school fees.
3. No, second graders should not put their names on their glue, but fifth graders should.
4. A first-grade student should purchase a 4-oz. glue bottle.
5. Answers will vary.
6. The notebook paper for third through fifth grades should be wide-ruled.
7. You know that wide-ruled is important because it is underlined.
8. Answers will vary.
9. The size of storage bags is different for boys and girls.
10. Answers will vary.
11. Billy's sister will need a compass and a protractor, and Billy will not.
12. Second-grade scissors can have points.
13. The pencils must be sharpened before bringing them to school.
14.–15. Answers will vary.

Page 26: Boys and Girls Club

1. Basketball, soccer, and volleyball are played at this club.
2. Free shoot-around is offered at the same time and night.
3. There are no events if the calendar says "no activities scheduled."
4. Events may change because of weather or unexpected occurrences.
5. The (M) indicates the main gym.
6. No events are scheduled because of the Valentine's Day Dance.
7. On February 10, the main gym has soccer and the auxiliary gym has basketball.
8.–9. Answers will vary.
10. All times shown are P.M.
11. Yes, two activities are in the same gym on February 6.
12. There are more activities for girls.
13. One gym is listed when there is only one activity.
14. Answers will vary.
15. Eleven nights have two events.

Page 30: The Bluebird

1. The combination platter is the most expensive appetizer.
2. To get garlic bread, you could order pasta or salad.
3. French fries, onion rings, cottage cheese, or applesauce is included with a sandwich.
4. A chicken sandwich and baked potato would cost $6.49.
5. Hamburger toppings are tomato, lettuce, cheese, and onion.
6. Children 12 and under can order from the children's menu.
7. You ask your server for the types of pies offered.
8. Six customers should order three pieces of cheesecake.
9. Spicy salad or pork chops are good options for people who like spicy food.
10. The least expensive meal for a fifteen-year-old is a house salad. For a ten-year-old, it is a hot dog.
11. A filet is 10 oz. for $13, and a baby filet is 6 oz. for $11.
12. Magnificent Chicken contains cheese sauce, pasta, and chicken.
13. She will get two pork chops.
14. Personal checks are not accepted.
15. Answers will vary.

Page 34: Super-Duper Pizza

1. Eight slices of American cheese are needed for this recipe.
2. The first thing to do after the dough, sauce, and hamburger are ready is to preheat the oven.
3. The sauce ingredients are tomato paste, tomato sauce, and sugar.
4. There are 500 calories in two slices.
5. Low heat is needed for the hamburger.
6. The dough takes the most time to prepare.
7. Answers will vary.
8. You would have 4 oz. left.
9. You need an 8-oz. package.
10. The sauce gets the most sugar.
11. There is a four minute difference between the bake time and preparation time.
12. You must first cut the American cheese into $1/4$"-wide strips.
13. If you ate the whole pizza, you would eat 40 g of carbohydrates.
14. A half an inch of dough should be left without sauce.
15. The first step to make the dough is to mix the flour and oil.

Page 38: Ian's Birthday

1. The invitation announces Ian's birthday party.
2. If arriving from Garfield Street, you stay on it until it ends.
3. Park Roadway is the road in the park.
4. Hillside Drive turns into Houston Avenue.
5. Depending on where you're coming from, follow the directions on the invitation to get to Ian's party.
6. Kent Street leads to the back entrance.
7. The party is taking place at Forest Dale Park.
8. You must turn left at the stop sign when entering the park from Brighton Road.
9. The front entrance is on Brighton Road.
10. The event is at pavilion #7. You will know it is the right one because there will be a sign that reads, "Ian's Party."
11. You travel on Garfield Street before turning onto Rockford Street.
12. There are two entrances to the park.
13. Spring Park Road turns into Brighton Road at a stoplight.
14.–15. Answers will vary.

Page 42: U. R. Smart Elementary

1. Fourteen extracurricular activities are offered at this school.
2. Spelling Bowl meets during September through November.
3. Seven activities are available to third graders.
4. First graders can join three activities.
5. Student Council meets from September through May in the morning of the first Thursday of the month.
6. No, a student couldn't participate in both Student Council and Choir, because they both meet on Thursday morning.
7. Thomas will be sending out information about Math Bowl.
8. All P.M. activities begin at 3:15.
9. Wee Ensemble and Winter Club both meet on Fridays.
10. Johnson sponsors the most activities.
11. Drama Club is sponsored by Meadow and Matlock in second grade and by Mason and Garrett in third and fourth grades.
12. Yearbook meets during September through May before school on the second Thursday of the month.
13. Track meets two to three days a week.
14.–15. Answers will vary.

Page 46: Busy Bee Elementary

1. The first time someone gets in trouble at recess, he gets a warning.
2. Yes, they can play two-hand touch football.
3. In severe weather, recess will be held inside the building.
4. When a student gets in trouble four or more times, she goes to the principal's office, her parents are called, and she is suspended from recess.
5. All students go to recess unless they have a parent/guardian's note.
6. If the playground is wet, students can play on blacktop areas only.
7. Answers will vary.
8. Students cannot tackle in football.
9. A severe problem will be treated as a fourth violation.
10. A doctor's note is needed if a student stays out of recess for more than three days.
11. Wrestling, tripping, and fighting are not allowed on the playground.
12. Students on swings can't stand or jump.
13. A parent would get a note if their child got in trouble a third time.
14. The student must return a basketball he takes out at recess.
15. On cold days, students without coats will go to study hall.

Page 50: Funville Sports Camp

1. Basketball, baseball, softball, flag football, contact football, and cheerleading are offered.
2. Boys and girls in third and fourth grades can attend this camp.
3. If you wanted to attend from June 28–July 2, you would sign up for the fourth session.
4. One session lasts for five days.
5. Call Steve Fuller if you have questions.
6. Two sessions will cost $220.
7. The deposit is $20.
8. Before camp, a camper must have a physical on file.
9. Funville Sports Camp is held at Funville Sports Complex.
10. No, campers are separated by sport.
11. Yes, Pedro can attend session #3.
12. Experienced coaches and staff will work with the campers.
13. Send the application and deposit to the Funville High School Athletic Department.
14. Campers should be picked up at 5:30 P.M.
15. Answers will vary.

Page 54: Dinosaureum Field Trip
1. The trip is Thursday, November 11.
2. The people leave school at 8:30 A.M.
3. Answers will vary.
4. The doctor's name and phone number are required.
5. Students should bring $5, a backpack, and a sack lunch.
6. The parent must have a background check completed and approved.
7. Answers will vary.
8. Answers will vary.
9. Students will arrive back at school at 3:30 P.M.
10. A second emergency person is needed in case the first person can't be reached.
11. The person's name, phone number, and relationship to the student are needed.
12. Students should not bring electronic devices.
13. Answers will vary.
14. It takes about three weeks to process a background check.
15. The parent would sign the form twice to be a chaperone.

Page 58: Jazzville Journal
1. Answers will vary.
2. Ms. Buggy's picnic is ruined because humans showed up.
3. Mr. Boxley's class would like to hike, swim, and eat on the picnic.
4. Ms. Buggy's class wants to eat.
5.-7. Answers will vary.
8. Mr. Boxley's class picnic is ruined because ants take over the food.
9. Mr. Boxley means that the ants like the picnic, too.
10.-11. Answers will vary.
12. The ants comic could not happen.
13.-15. Answers will vary.

END of Open-Ended Format

Answer Key—Mixed Format

Page 7: Honesty Pays
1. c. Anne Longlunger
2. False
3. True
4. a. Alice Sampson
5. Ridgeville, Indiana
6. a. December 22
7. False
8. c. $2,000
9. Alice found the wallet under a clothing rack in a store.
10. b. turned it in at the store office
11. True
12. a. giving
13. c. She felt it was the right thing to do.
14.-15. Answers will vary.

Page 11: Washington Elementary
1. c. December
2. December 10
3. False
4. b. near the snowflakes
5. a. 2–3
6. December 10 is a half day for students.
7. macaroni & cheese and green beans
8. Those are weekend days.
9. a. December 18
10. True
11. c. beef
12. b. 10
13. True
14. December 4, 13, and 18
15. Answers will vary.

Page 15: Exploring the Universe
1. False
2. d. 2–8
3. game board, 1 die, answer key, storage box, 60 Challenge Cards, 8 game pieces, 60 Asteroid Cards, and game rule sheet
4. True
5. False
6. a. an Asteroid Box
7. b. the Space Station
8. Asteroid Card
9. False
10. False
11. Answers will vary.
12. a. A player reaches Earth.
13. a. Earth
14. Answers will vary.
15. c. storage box

Page 19: Get-Up-Early Specials
1. c. Saturday
2. Answers will vary.
3. kids' jackets and coats, girls' tops and skirts
4. a. Gentry train sets
5. True
6. toys
7. d. 2
8. Rugged Racer, Cool BMX, Zapitron
9. a. 60%
10. False
11. True
12. Answers will vary.
13. c. 3
14. d. 13" TVs
15. leather jacket, bikes

Page 23: Eagle Elementary
1. False
2. False
3. no; yes
4. c. 4 oz.
5. Answers will vary.
6. a. It is wide ruled
7. underlined
8. False
9. The size of storage bag is different.
10. Answers will vary.
11. True
12. True
13. d. both a and c
14.-15. Answers will vary.

Page 27: Boys and Girls Club
1. d. all of the above
2. False
3. 7, 11, 21, 28
4. d. both a and b
5. True
6. Valentine's Day Dance
7. Girls' indoor soccer; boys' basketball
8. True
9. Answers will vary.
10. False
11. 6
12. b. girls
13. There is only one activity.
14. Answers will vary.
15. c. 11

Page 31: The Bluebird
1. Combination Platter
2. salad; pasta
3. False
4. d. $6.49
5. True
6. d. both a and b
7. False
8. d. 3
9. pork chops; spicy salad
10. house salad; hot dog
11. False
12. b. Magnificent Chicken
13. 2
14. False
15. Answers will vary.

Page 35: Super-Duper Pizza
1. d. 8
2. preheat
3. tomato paste, tomato sauce, sugar
4. a. 500
5. True
6. dough
7. False
8. True
9. b. 8 ounces
10. False
11. False
12. c. Sprinkle on the hamburger.
13. a. 40
14. $^1/_2$
15. The first thing you do when making the dough is mix the flour and oil.

Page 39: Ian's Birthday
1. Ian's birthday party
2. True
3. b. Park Roadway
4. Houston Avenue
5. Depending on where you're coming from, follow the directions.
6. Kent Street
7. Forest Dale
8. You turn left at the stop sign.
9. True
10. b. A sign will read "Ian's Party."
11. b. Garfield Street
12. two
13. False
14.-15. Answers will vary.

Page 43: U. R. Smart Elementary
1. a. Fourteen
2. False
3. a. 7
4. False
5. d. Sept.-May, 1st Thurs. of month, A.M.
6. No, a student can't participate in both Student Council and Choir, because they both meet on Thursday.
7. Thomas
8. False
9. Wee Ensemble; Winter Club
10. c. Johnson
11. b. Mason/Garrett, Meadow/Matlock
12. d. Sept.-May, 2nd Thurs. of month, A.M.
13. 2-3
14.-15. Answers will vary.

Page 47: Busy Bee Elementary
1. c. warning
2. True
3. b. classrooms
4. suspended from recess
5. note from a parent/guardian
6. True
7. Answers will vary.
8. a. tackle
9. d. 4th
10. 3
11. wrestling, tripping, fighting
12. stand; jump
13. b. a note home
14. Students
15. c. study hall

Page 51: Funville Sports Camp
1. basketball, baseball, softball, flag football, contact football, cheerleading
2. d. boys and girls in 3rd and 4th grades
3. True
4. c. 5 days
5. call Steve Fuller
6. b. $220.00
7. True
8. c. get a physical
9. b. sports complex
10. False
11. yes; #3
12. b. coaches and staff
13. True
14. a. 5:30 P.M.
15. Answers will vary.

Page 55: Dinosaureum Field Trip
1. b. November 11
2. False
3. False
4. name; phone number
5. c. both a and b
6. approved
7. Answers will vary.
8. True
9. 3:30 P.M.
10. A second emergency person is needed in case the first person can't be reached.
11. her name, phone number, and relationship to the student
12. c. an electronic device
13. Answers will vary.
14. False
15. 2

Page 59: Jazzville Journal
1. a. excited
2. b. show up
3. hike; swim; eat
4. eat
5. Answers will vary.
6. a. the way you see a certain situation
7. False
8. c. cover the food
9. False
10. True
11. Answers will vary.
12. b. Ms. Buggy's class picnic
13. Answers will vary.
14. True
15. Answers will vary.